Clarinet
Scales, Arpeggios & Exercises

for Trinity College London
Clarinet & Jazz Clarinet
exams from 2015

Grades 1-8

Published by
Trinity College London Press Ltd
trinitycollege.com

Registered in England
Company no. 09726123

Printed in England by Caligraving Ltd

Grade 1

Clarinet candidates to prepare *either* section i) *or* section ii) in full				
either i) Scales & arpeggios (from memory) – the examiner will select from the following:				
Scales: F and G major A minor (candidate's choice of *either* harmonic *or* melodic *or* natural minor) **Arpeggios:** F and G major A minor	one octave	min. tempi: scales: ♩=72 arpeggios: ♪=120	tongued *or* slurred	*mf*
***or* ii) Exercises** (music may be used):				
Candidate to prepare 1a *or* 1b; 2a *or* 2b; and 3a *or* 3b (three exercises in total).				
The candidate will choose one exercise to play first; the examiner will then select one of the remaining two prepared exercises to be performed.				
1a. Going Through a Phrase *or* 1b. A Soft Drum			for tone and phrasing	
2a. Chalk and Cheese *or* 2b. Answering Back			for articulation	
3a. Relaxing *or* 3b. Steady Now!			for finger technique	

Jazz clarinet candidates to prepare *either* section i) *or* section ii) in full				
either i) Scales & arpeggios (from memory) – the examiner will select from the following:				
Using the tonal/modal centre G: Major scale followed by major 7th arpeggio Dorian scale followed by minor 7th arpeggio	one octave	min. tempi: scales: ♩=72 7ths: ♩=60	straight *or* swung (♫ = ♩♪)	*mf*
***or* ii) Exercises** (music may be used):				
Candidate to prepare 1a *or* 1b; 2a *or* 2b; and 3a *or* 3b (three exercises in total).				
The candidate will choose one exercise to play first; the examiner will then select one of the remaining two prepared exercises to be performed.				
1a. Going Through a Phrase *or* 1b. A Soft Drum			for tone and phrasing	
2a. Chalk and Cheese *or* 2b. Answering Back			for articulation	
3a. Relaxing *or* 3b. Steady Now!			for finger technique	

i) Scales & Arpeggios

F major scale (one octave)

F major arpeggio (one octave)

G major scale (one octave)‡

G major arpeggio (one octave)

G major 7th arpeggio (one octave)*

Dorian scale on G (one octave)*

G minor 7th arpeggio (one octave)*

A harmonic minor scale (one octave)

A melodic minor scale (one octave)

A natural minor scale (one octave)

A minor arpeggio (one octave)

ii) Exercises

1a. Going Through a Phrase – tone and phrasing

1b. A Soft Drum – tone and phrasing

2a. Chalk and Cheese – articulation

2b. Answering Back – articulation

3a. Relaxing – finger technique

3b. Steady Now! – finger technique

Grade 2

Clarinet candidates to prepare *either* section i) *or* section ii) in full

either i) **Scales & arpeggios** (from memory) – the examiner will select from the following:

Scales:			
F major G minor (candidate's choice of *either* harmonic *or* melodic *or* natural minor)	two octaves	min. tempi: scales: ♩=72 arpeggios: ♪=120	tongued *or* slurred	*mf*
C major	to 12th			
E minor (candidate's choice of *either* harmonic *or* melodic *or* natural minor)	one octave			
Arpeggios: F major G minor	two octaves			
C major	to 12th			
E minor	one octave			

or ii) **Exercises** (music may be used):

Candidate to prepare 1a *or* 1b; 2a *or* 2b; and 3a *or* 3b (three exercises in total).

The candidate will choose one exercise to play first; the examiner will then select one of the remaining two prepared exercises to be performed.

1a. Snake in a Basket	*or*	1b. D-lightful	for tone and phrasing
2a. Vive la Difference	*or*	2b. One Man Band	for articulation
3a. The Sphinx	*or*	3b. A Cloudy Day	for finger technique

Jazz clarinet candidates to prepare *either* section i) *or* section ii) in full

either i) **Scales & arpeggios** (from memory) – the examiner will select from the following:

Using the tonal/modal centre D:		min. tempi: scales: ♩=72 arpeggios: ♪=120 7ths: ♩=60	straight *or* swung (♫ = ♩³♪)	tongued *or* slurred	*mf*
Major scale followed by major 7th arpeggio Dorian scale followed by minor 7th arpeggio Mixolydian scale followed by major arpeggio with a lowered 7th (D⁷)	one octave				

or ii) **Exercises** (music may be used):

Candidate to prepare 1a *or* 1b; 2a *or* 2b; and 3a *or* 3b (three exercises in total).

The candidate will choose one exercise to play first; the examiner will then select one of the remaining two prepared exercises to be performed.

1a. Snake in a Basket	*or*	1b. D-lightful	for tone and phrasing
2a. Vive la Difference	*or*	2b. One Man Band	for articulation
3a. The Sphinx	*or*	3b. A Cloudy Day	for finger technique

i) Scales & Arpeggios

C major scale (to 12th)

C major arpeggio (to 12th)

D major scale (one octave)*

D major 7th arpeggio (one octave)*

Dorian scale on D (one octave)*

D minor 7th arpeggio (one octave)*

Mixolydian scale on D (one octave)*

D major arpeggio with a lowered 7th (D⁷) (one octave)*

E harmonic minor scale (one octave)

E melodic minor scale (one octave)

Grade 2 continued

E natural minor scale (one octave)

E minor arpeggio (one octave)

F major scale (two octaves)

F major arpeggio (two octaves)

G harmonic minor scale (two octaves)

G melodic minor scale (two octaves)

G natural minor scale (two octaves)

G minor arpeggio (two octaves)

ii) Exercises

1a. Snake in a Basket – tone and phrasing

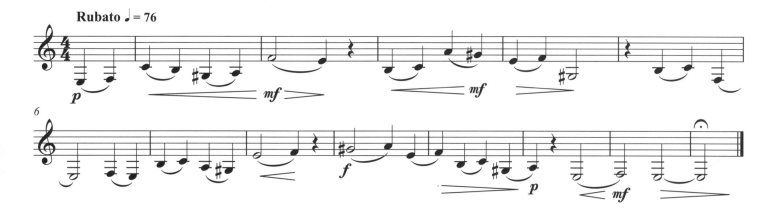

1b. D-lightful – tone and phrasing

2a. Vive la Difference – articulation

2b. One Man Band – articulation

3a. The Sphinx – finger technique

3b. A Cloudy Day – finger technique

Grade 3

<table>
<tr><td colspan="5">Clarinet candidates to prepare either section i) or section ii) in full</td></tr>
<tr><td colspan="5">either i) Scales & arpeggios (from memory) – the examiner will select from the following:</td></tr>
<tr>
<td>Scales:
C and B♭ major
A minor (candidate's choice of either harmonic or melodic or natural minor)</td>
<td>two octaves</td>
<td rowspan="6">min. tempi:
scales:
♩=84

arpeggios:
♪=132</td>
<td rowspan="6">tongued or slurred</td>
<td rowspan="6">mf</td>
</tr>
<tr>
<td>D minor (candidate's choice of either harmonic or melodic or natural minor)</td>
<td>to 12th</td>
</tr>
<tr>
<td>A major
Chromatic scale starting on G</td>
<td>one octave</td>
</tr>
<tr>
<td>Arpeggios:
C and B♭ major
A minor</td>
<td>two octaves</td>
</tr>
<tr>
<td>D minor</td>
<td>to 12th</td>
</tr>
<tr>
<td>A major</td>
<td>one octave</td>
</tr>
<tr><td colspan="5">or ii) Exercises (music may be used):</td></tr>
<tr><td colspan="5">Candidate to prepare 1a or 1b; 2a or 2b; and 3a or 3b (three exercises in total).
The candidate will choose one exercise to play first; the examiner will then select one of the remaining two prepared exercises to be performed.</td></tr>
<tr><td colspan="2">1a. Whistling a Tune   or   1b. Meandering</td><td colspan="3">for tone and phrasing</td></tr>
<tr><td colspan="2">2a. Hit It!   or   2b. Hot and Cold</td><td colspan="3">for articulation</td></tr>
<tr><td colspan="2">3a. Wandering   or   3b. Dig the Digit!</td><td colspan="3">for finger technique</td></tr>
</table>

<table>
<tr><td colspan="6">Jazz clarinet candidates to prepare either section i) or section ii) in full</td></tr>
<tr><td colspan="6">either i) Scales & arpeggios (from memory) – the examiner will select from the following:</td></tr>
<tr>
<td>Using the tonal/modal centre F, starting on the lowest F:
Major scale followed by major 7th arpeggio
Dorian scale followed by minor 7th arpeggio
Mixolydian scale followed by major arpeggio with a lowered 7th (F⁷)</td>
<td>two octaves</td>
<td rowspan="2">min. tempi:
scales: ♩=84
arpeggios: ♪=132
7ths: ♩=66</td>
<td rowspan="2">straight or swung
(♫ = ♪³♪)</td>
<td rowspan="2">tongued or slurred</td>
<td rowspan="2">mf</td>
</tr>
<tr>
<td>Pentatonic minor scale</td>
<td>one octave</td>
</tr>
<tr><td colspan="6">or ii) Exercises (music may be used):</td></tr>
<tr><td colspan="6">Candidate to prepare 1a or 1b; 2a or 2b; and 3a or 3b (three exercises in total).
The candidate will choose one exercise to play first; the examiner will then select one of the remaining two prepared exercises to be performed.</td></tr>
<tr><td colspan="3">1a. Whistling a Tune   or   1b. Meandering</td><td colspan="3">for tone and phrasing</td></tr>
<tr><td colspan="3">2a. Hit It!   or   2b. Hot and Cold</td><td colspan="3">for articulation</td></tr>
<tr><td colspan="3">3a. Wandering   or   3b. Dig the Digit!</td><td colspan="3">for finger technique</td></tr>
</table>

i) Scales & Arpeggios

C major scale (two octaves)

C major arpeggio (two octaves)

Grade 3 continued

D harmonic minor scale (to 12th)

D melodic minor scale (to 12th)

D natural minor scale (to 12th)

D minor arpeggio (to 12th)

F major scale (two octaves)*

F major 7th arpeggio (two octaves)*

Dorian scale on F (two octaves)*

F minor 7th arpeggio (two octaves)*

Mixolydian scale on F (two octaves)*

F major arpeggio with a lowered 7th (F⁷) (two octaves)*

F pentatonic minor scale (one octave)*

Chromatic scale starting on G (one octave)

A major scale (one octave)

A major arpeggio (one octave)

A harmonic minor scale (two octaves)

A melodic minor scale (two octaves)

A natural minor scale (two octaves)

A minor arpeggio (two octaves)

Grade 3 continued

Bb major scale (two octaves)

Bb major arpeggio (two octaves)

ii) Exercises

1a. Whistling a Tune – tone and phrasing

1b. Meandering – tone and phrasing

2a. Hit It! – articulation

2b. Hot and Cold – articulation

3a. Wandering – finger technique

3b. Dig the Digit! – finger technique

Grade 4

Clarinet candidates to prepare *either* section i) *or* section ii) in full					
either i) **Scales & arpeggios** (from memory) – the examiner will select from the following:					
Scales: G, D and A major E (starting on low E), B and G minor (candidate's choice of *either* harmonic *or* melodic *or* natural minor)	two octaves	min. tempi: scales: ♩=96 arpeggios: ♪=138 7ths: ♩=69	tongued *or* slurred		*mf*
Chromatic scale starting on F					
Pentatonic (major) scale starting on G (candidate's choice of starting G)	one octave				
Arpeggios: G, D and A major E (starting on low E), B and G minor	two octaves				
Dominant 7th arpeggio in the key of C					
or ii) **Exercises** (music may be used):					
Candidate to prepare 1a *or* 1b; 2a *or* 2b; and 3a *or* 3b (three exercises in total). The candidate will choose one exercise to play first; the examiner will then select one of the remaining two prepared exercises to be performed.					
1a. Express Yourself *or* 1b. Rephrase That		for tone and phrasing			
2a. Scat! *or* 2b. Haiku		for articulation			
3a. Arpeggiate *or* 3b. Fair Comment		for finger technique			

Jazz clarinet candidates to prepare *either* section i) *or* section ii) in full					
either i) **Scales & arpeggios** (from memory) – the examiner will select from the following:					
Using the tonal/modal centre C: Major scale followed by major 7th arpeggio Dorian scale followed by minor 7th arpeggio Mixolydian scale followed by major arpeggio with a lowered 7th (C⁷) Pentatonic minor scale Melodic *or* jazz melodic minor scale followed by minor arpeggio with major 7th Chromatic scale	two octaves	min. tempi: scales: ♩=96 arpeggios: ♪=138 7ths: ♩=69	straight *or* swung (♫ = ♩³♪)	tongued *or* slurred	*mf*
or ii) **Exercises** (music may be used):					
Candidate to prepare 1a *or* 1b; 2a *or* 2b; and 3a *or* 3b (three exercises in total). The candidate will choose one exercise to play first; the examiner will then select one of the remaining two prepared exercises to be performed.					
1a. Express Yourself *or* 1b. Rephrase That		for tone and phrasing			
2a. Scat! *or* 2b. Haiku		for articulation			
3a. Arpeggiate *or* 3b. Fair Comment		for finger technique			

i) Scales & Arpeggios

C major scale (two octaves)*

C major 7th arpeggio (two octaves)*

Grade 4 continued

Dorian scale on C (two octaves)*

C minor 7th arpeggio (two octaves)*

Mixolydian scale on C (two octaves)*

C major arpeggio with a lowered 7th (C⁷) (two octaves)*

C pentatonic minor scale (two octaves)*

C melodic minor scale (two octaves)*

C jazz melodic minor scale (two octaves)*

C minor arpeggio with a major 7th (two octaves)*

Chromatic scale starting on C (two octaves)*

Dominant 7th arpeggio in the key of C (two octaves)

D major scale (two octaves)

D major arpeggio (two octaves)

E harmonic minor scale (two octaves)

E melodic minor scale (two octaves)

E natural minor scale (two octaves)

Grade 4 continued

E minor arpeggio (two octaves)

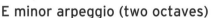

Chromatic scale starting on F (two octaves)

G major scale (two octaves)

G major arpeggio (two octaves)

G harmonic minor scale (two octaves)

G melodic minor scale (two octaves)

G natural minor scale (two octaves)

G minor arpeggio (two octaves)

G pentatonic major scale (one octave)

or

A major scale (two octaves)

A major arpeggio (two octaves)

B harmonic minor scale (two octaves)

B melodic minor scale (two octaves)

B natural minor scale (two octaves)

B minor arpeggio (two octaves)

ii) Exercises

1a. Express Yourself – tone and phrasing

1b. Rephrase That – tone and phrasing

2a. Scat! – articulation

2b. Haiku – articulation

3a. Arpeggiate – finger technique

3b. Fair Comment – finger technique

Grade 5

Clarinet candidates to prepare *either* section i) *or* section ii) in full

either i) Scales & arpeggios (from memory) – the examiner will select from the following:

Scales & Arpeggios				
Scales: A, E, A♭ and E♭ major C, F, C♯ and F♯ minor (candidate's choice of *either* harmonic *or* melodic *or* natural minor)				
Chromatic scale starting on E (starting on low E) Pentatonic (major) scale starting on C	two octaves	min. tempi: scales: ♩=116 arpeggios: ♪=152 7ths: ♩=76	tongued *or* slurred	*mf*
Arpeggios: A, E, A♭ and E♭ major C, F, C♯ and F♯ minor				
Dominant 7th arpeggios in the keys of G and D Diminished 7th arpeggio starting on G				

or ii) Exercises (music may be used):

Candidate to prepare 1a *or* 1b; 2a *or* 2b; and 3a *or* 3b (three exercises in total).

The candidate will choose one exercise to play first; the examiner will then select one of the remaining two prepared exercises to be performed.

1a. Lilt	*or*	1b. Sequences	for tone and phrasing
2a. A Conversation	*or*	2b. Got the Blues	for articulation
3a. Gliding	*or*	3b. Hide and Seek	for finger technique

Jazz clarinet candidates to prepare *either* section i) *or* section ii) in full

either i) Scales & arpeggios (from memory) – the examiner will select from the following:

Scales & Arpeggios					
Using the tonal/modal centre of *either* low E *or* A at the candidate's choice: Major scale followed by major 7th arpeggio Dorian scale followed by minor 7th arpeggio Mixolydian scale followed by major arpeggio with a lowered 7th (E^7 *or* A^7) Pentatonic major *and* minor scale Chromatic scale Blues scale Diminished 7th arpeggio	two octaves	min. tempi: scales: ♩=116 arpeggios: ♪=152 7ths: ♩=76	straight *or* swung (♫ = ♩³♪)	tongued *or* slurred	*mf*

or ii) Exercises (music may be used):

Candidate to prepare 1a *or* 1b; 2a *or* 2b; and 3a *or* 3b (three exercises in total).

The candidate will choose one exercise to play first; the examiner will then select one of the remaining two prepared exercises to be performed.

1a. Lilt	*or*	1b. Sequences	for tone and phrasing
2a. A Conversation	*or*	2b. Got the Blues	for articulation
3a. Gliding	*or*	3b. Hide and Seek	for finger technique

i) Scales & Arpeggios

C harmonic minor scale (two octaves)

C melodic minor scale (two octaves)

C natural minor scale (two octaves)

C minor arpeggio (two octaves)

C pentatonic major scale (two octaves)

C# harmonic minor scale (two octaves)

C# melodic minor scale (two octaves)

C# natural minor scale (two octaves)

Grade 5 continued

C# minor arpeggio (two octaves)

Dominant 7th arpeggio in the key of D (two octaves)

Eb major scale (two octaves)

Eb major arpeggio (two octaves)

E major scale (two octaves)‡

E major arpeggio (two octaves)

E major 7th arpeggio (two octaves)*

Dorian scale on E (two octaves)*

E minor 7th arpeggio (two octaves)*

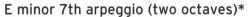

Mixolydian on E (two octaves)*

E major arpeggio with a lowered 7th (E^7) (two octaves)*

E pentatonic major scale (two octaves)*

E pentatonic minor scale (two octaves)*

Chromatic scale starting on E (two octaves)‡

Blues scale on E (two octaves)*

Grade 5 continued

Diminished 7th arpeggio starting on E (two octaves)*

F harmonic minor scale (two octaves)

F melodic minor scale (two octaves)

F natural minor scale (two octaves)

F minor arpeggio (two octaves)

F# harmonic minor scale (two octaves)

F# melodic minor scale (two octaves)

F♯ natural minor scale (two octaves)

F♯ minor arpeggio (two octaves)

Dominant 7th arpeggio in the key of G (two octaves)

Diminished 7th arpeggio starting on G (two octaves)

A♭ major scale (two octaves)

A♭ major arpeggio (two octaves)

A major scale (two octaves)‡

Grade 5 continued

A major arpeggio (two octaves)

A major 7th arpeggio (two octaves)*

Dorian scale on A (two octaves)*

A minor 7th arpeggio (two octaves)*

Mixolydian scale on A (two octaves)*

A major arpeggio with a lowered 7th (A^7) (two octaves)*

A pentatonic major scale (two octaves)*

A pentatonic minor scale (two octaves)*

Chromatic scale starting on A (two octaves)*

Blues scale on A (two octaves)*

Diminished 7th arpeggio on A (two octaves)*

ii) Exercises

1a. Lilt – tone and phrasing

Grade 5 continued

1b. Sequences – tone and phrasing

2a. A Conversation – articulation

I've got the rhythm and I've got the blues Yeh!

2b. Got the Blues – articulation

bí doo bí doo bí   Yeh
doo bí, dah bí do

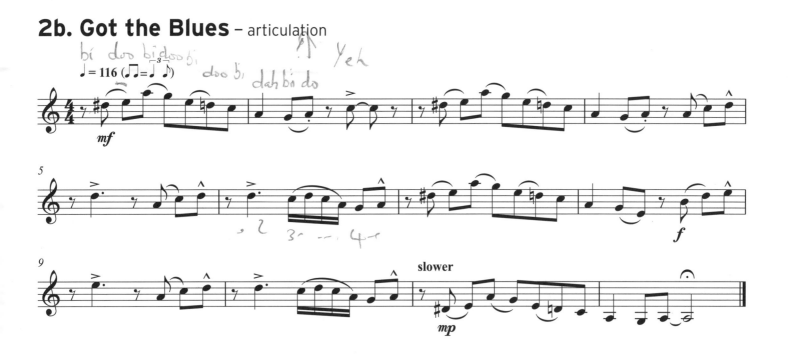

3a. Gliding – finger technique

3b. Hide and Seek – finger technique

Grade 6

Clarinet candidates to prepare *either* section i) *or* section ii) in full

either i) Scales & arpeggios (from memory) – the examiner will select from the following:

Candidates should prepare scales and arpeggios from the following tonal centres: F major, F minor	three octaves			
A major, A minor Db major, C# minor	two octaves	min. tempi: scales: ♩=120 arpeggios: ♩.=63 7ths: ♩=96	tongued, slurred *or* staccato-tongued	*f or p*
Plus: Chromatic scale starting on F Diminished 7th arpeggio starting on F	three octaves			
Pentatonic (major) scale starting on Db Whole-tone scale starting on A Dominant 7th arpeggio in the key of F#	two octaves			

When the examiner requests a **major tonal centre**, the candidate should play in succession:

  The major scale
  The major arpeggio

When the examiner requests a **minor tonal centre**, the candidate should play in succession:

  The melodic minor scale
  The harmonic minor scale
  The minor arpeggio

or ii) Orchestral extracts

See current syllabus for details

Jazz clarinet candidates to prepare *either* section i) *or* section ii) in full

either i) Scales & arpeggios (from memory) – the examiner will select from the following:

Using the tonal/modal centres F, A and Db/C#: Major scale followed by major 7th arpeggio Dorian scale followed by minor 7th arpeggio Mixolydian scale followed by major arpeggio with a lowered 7th (F⁷, A⁷ and Db⁷)	F: three octaves A & C#: two octaves	min. tempi: scales: ♩=120 arpeggios: ♩.=63 7ths: ♩=96	straight *or* swung (♫ = ♩³♪)	tongued, slurred *or* staccato-tongued (straight scales only)	*f or p*
Chromatic scale starting on F Diminished 7th arpeggio starting on F	three octaves			
Pentatonic (major) scale starting on C# Blues scale starting on A	two octaves			

or ii) Study

See current syllabus for details

Db major scale (two octaves)‡

Db major arpeggio (two octaves)

Grade 6 continued

Db major 7th arpeggio (two octaves)*

C# harmonic minor scale (two octaves) – see Grade 5

C# melodic minor scale (two octaves) – see Grade 5

C# minor arpeggio (two octaves) – see Grade 5

Dorian scale on C#/Db (two octaves)*

C# minor 7th arpeggio (two octaves)*

Mixolydian scale on Db/C# (two octaves)*

Db major arpeggio with a lowered 7th (Db⁷) (two octaves)*

Db/C# pentatonic major scale (two octaves)‡

F major scale (three octaves)‡

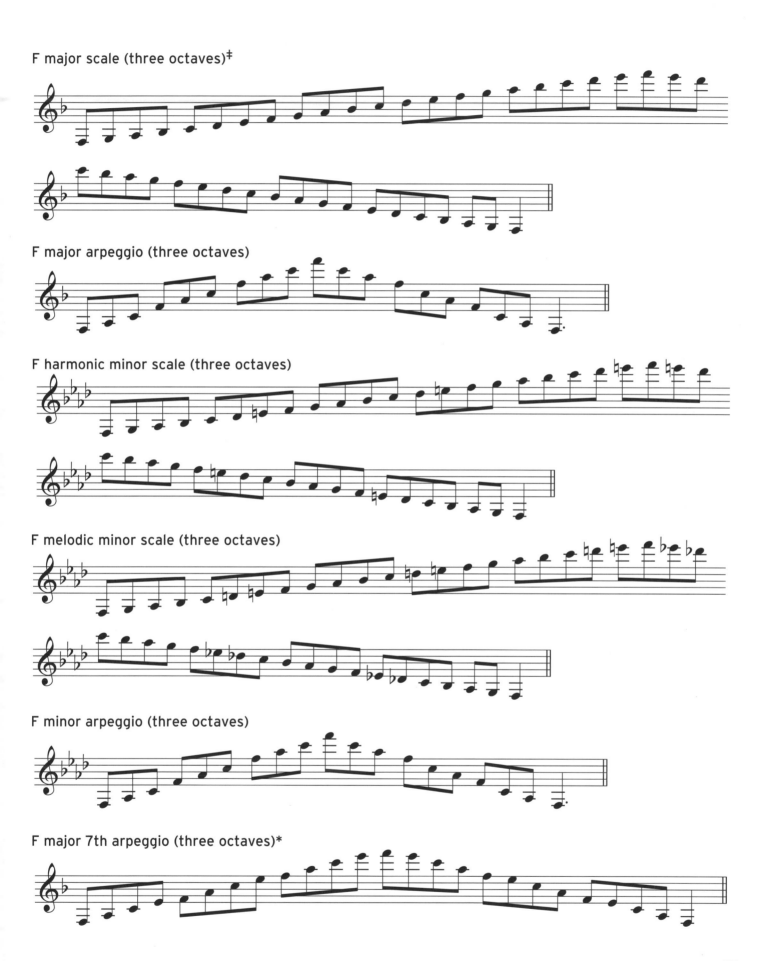

F major arpeggio (three octaves)

F harmonic minor scale (three octaves)

F melodic minor scale (three octaves)

F minor arpeggio (three octaves)

F major 7th arpeggio (three octaves)*

Grade 6 continued

Dorian scale on F (three octaves)*

F minor 7th arpeggio (three octaves)*

Mixolydian scale on F (three octaves)*

F major arpeggio with a lowered 7th (F⁷) (two octaves)* – see Grade 3

Chromatic scale starting on F (three octaves)‡

Diminished 7th arpeggio on F (three octaves)‡

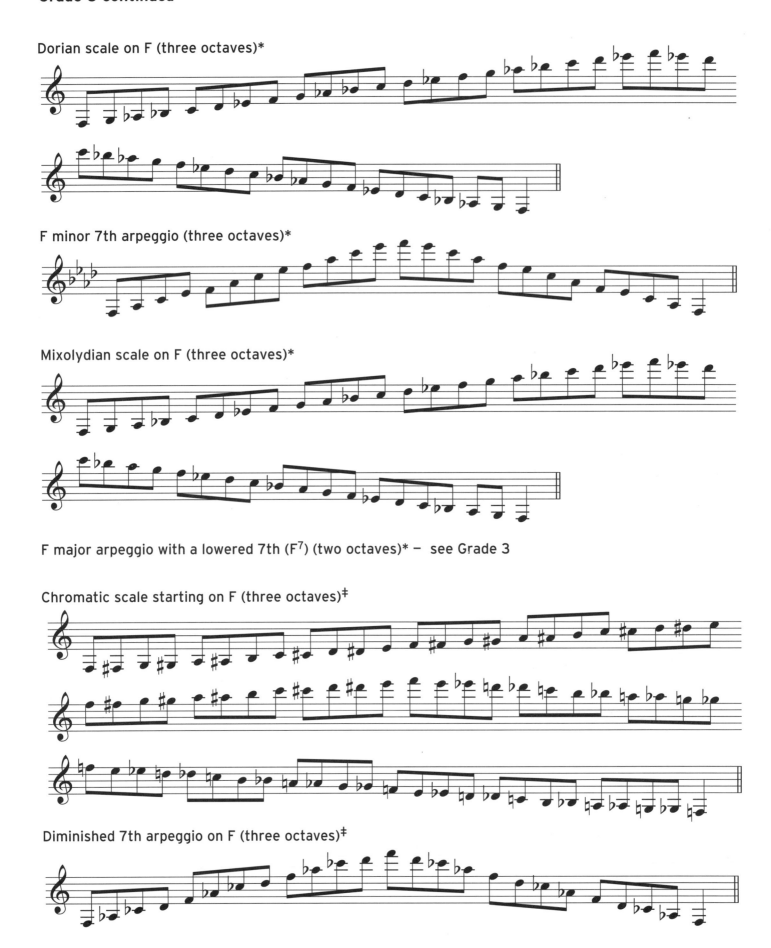

38

Dominant 7th arpeggio in the key of F♯ (two octaves)

A major scale (two octaves)‡ − see Grade 5

A major arpeggio (two octaves) − see Grade 5

A major 7th arpeggio (two octaves)* − see Grade 5

A harmonic minor scale (two octaves) − see Grade 3

A melodic minor scale (two octaves) − see Grade 3

A minor arpeggio (two octaves) − see Grade 3

Dorian scale on A (two octaves)* − see Grade 5

A minor 7th arpeggio (two octaves)* − see Grade 5

Mixolydian scale on A (two octaves)* − see Grade 5

A major arpeggio with a lowered 7th (A⁷) (two octaves)* − see Grade 5

A whole-tone scale (two octaves)

Blues scale on A (two octaves)* − see Grade 5

Grade 7

Clarinet candidates to prepare *either* section i) *or* section ii) in full

either **i) Scales & arpeggios** (from memory) − the examiner will select from the following:

Candidates should prepare scales and arpeggios from the following tonal centres: F♯ major, F♯ minor	three octaves	min. tempi: scales: ♩=132 arpeggios: ♩.=69 7ths: ♩=104	tongued, slurred *or* staccato- tongued	f *or* p
Bb major, Bb minor D major, D minor Eb major, Eb minor	two octaves			
Plus: Chromatic scale starting on F♯ Diminished 7th arpeggio starting on F♯	three octaves			
Pentatonic (major) scale starting on Bb and Eb Whole-tone scale starting on Eb Dominant 7th arpeggios in the keys of Eb and G Augmented arpeggio starting on D	two octaves			

When the examiner requests a **major tonal centre**, the candidate should play in succession:

   The major scale
   The major arpeggio

When the examiner requests a **minor tonal centre**, the candidate should play in succession:

   The melodic minor scale
   The harmonic minor scale
   The minor arpeggio

or **ii) Orchestral extracts**

See current syllabus for details

Jazz clarinet candidates to prepare *either* section i) *or* section ii) in full

either **i) Scales & arpeggios** (from memory) − the examiner will select from the following:

Using the tonal/modal centres F♯, Bb **and** D: Major scale followed by major 7th arpeggio Dorian scale followed by minor 7th arpeggio Mixolydian scale followed by major arpeggio with a lowered 7th (F♯[7], Bb[7] and D[7])	F♯: three octaves Bb & D: two octaves	min. tempi: scales: ♩=132 arpeggios: ♩.=69 7ths: ♩=104	straight *or* swung (♫ = ♩³♪)	tongued, slurred *or* staccato- tongued (straight scales only)	f *or* p
Using the tonal centre F♯: Jazz melodic minor scale followed by minor arpeggio with major 7th	three octaves			
Using the tonal centre D: Whole tone scale followed by augmented arpeggio	two octaves			
Chromatic scale starting on F♯ Diminished 7th arpeggio starting on F♯	three octaves			
Pentatonic (major) scale starting on Bb Pentatonic (minor) scale starting on D Blues scale starting on Bb	two octaves			

or **ii) Study**

See current syllabus for details

D major scale (two octaves)‡ − see Grade 4

D major arpeggio (two octaves) − see Grade 4

D major 7th arpeggio (two octaves)*

D harmonic minor scale (two octaves)

D melodic minor scale (two octaves)

D minor arpeggio (two octaves)

Augmented arpeggio on D (two octaves)*

D pentatonic minor scale (two octaves)*

Dorian scale on D (two octaves)*

Grade 7 continued

D minor 7th arpeggio (two octaves)*

Mixolydian scale on D (two octaves)*

D major arpeggio with a lowered 7th (D⁷) (two octaves)* – see Grade 2

Whole-tone scale on D (two octaves)*

E♭ major scale (two octaves) – see Grade 5

E♭ major arpeggio (two octaves) – see Grade 5

E♭ harmonic minor scale (two octaves)

E♭ melodic minor scale (two octaves)

E♭ minor arpeggio (two octaves)

Dominant 7th arpeggio in the key of E♭ (two octaves)

E♭ pentatonic major scale (two octaves)

Whole-tone scale on E♭ (two octaves)

F♯ major scale (three octaves)‡

F♯ major arpeggio (three octaves)

F♯ major 7th arpeggio (three octaves)*

F♯ harmonic minor scale (three octaves)

Grade 7 continued

F♯ melodic minor scale (three octaves)

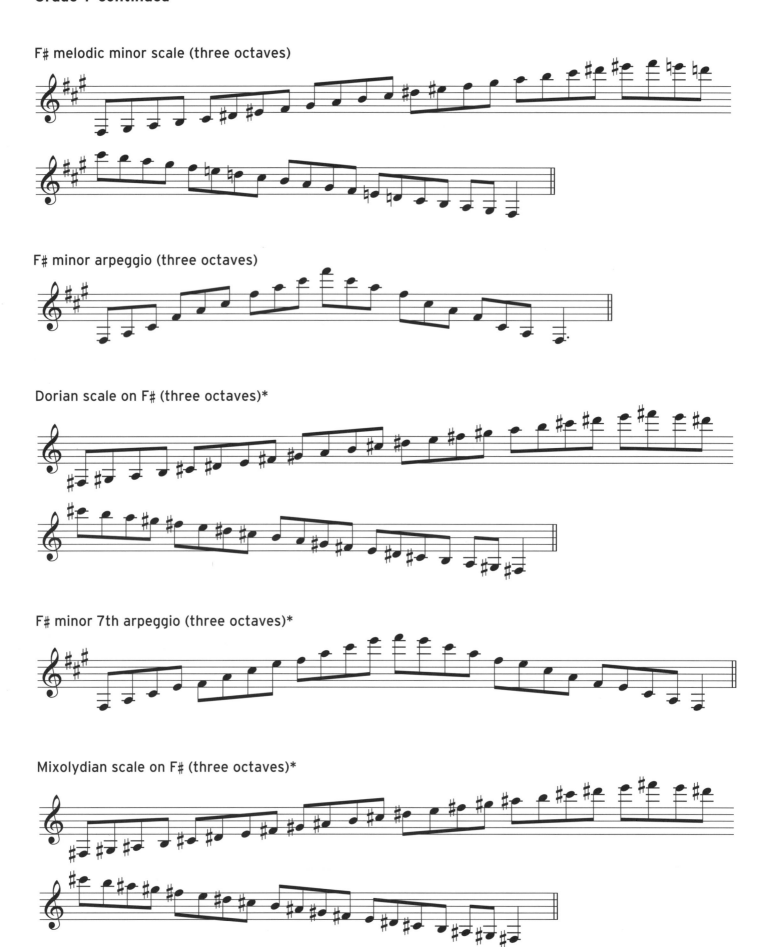

F♯ minor arpeggio (three octaves)

Dorian scale on F♯ (three octaves)*

F♯ minor 7th arpeggio (three octaves)*

Mixolydian scale on F♯ (three octaves)*

F# major arpeggio with a lowered 7th (F#7) (three octaves)*

F# jazz melodic minor scale (three octaves)*

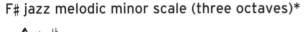

F# minor arpeggio with a major 7th (three octaves)*

Chromatic scale starting on F# (three octaves)‡

Diminished 7th arpeggio on F# (three octaves)‡

Dominant 7th arpeggio in the key of G (two octaves) – see Grade 5

Grade 7 continued

B♭ major scale (two octaves)‡ – see Grade 3

B♭ major arpeggio (two octaves) – see Grade 3

B♭ major 7th arpeggio (three octaves)*

B♭ harmonic minor scale (two octaves)

B♭ melodic minor scale (two octaves)

B♭ minor arpeggio (two octaves)

B♭ pentatonic major scale (two octaves)‡

Dorian scale on B♭ (two octaves)*

B♭ minor 7th arpeggio (two octaves)*

Mixolydian scale on B♭ (two octaves)*

B♭ major arpeggio with a lowered 7th (B♭^{7}) (two octaves)*

Blues scale on B♭ (two octaves)*

Grade 8

Clarinet candidates to prepare *either* section i) *or* section ii) in full

either i) Scales & arpeggios (from memory) – the examiner will select from the following:

Candidates should prepare scales and arpeggios from the following tonal centres: E major, E minor G major, G minor	three octaves	min. tempi: scales: ♩=132 arpeggios: ♩.=69 7ths: ♩=104	tongued, slurred, staccato- tongued *or* using mixed articulation*
A♭ major, G♯ minor C major, C minor B major, B minor	two octaves		
Plus: Chromatic scale starting on E Whole-tone scale starting on G Dominant 7th arpeggios in the keys of A and C Diminished 7th arpeggio starting on E	three octaves		
Pentatonic (major) scale starting on C Diminished 7th arpeggio starting on C Augmented arpeggio starting on A♭ and B	two octaves		

f or *p*

When the examiner requests a **major tonal centre**, the candidate should play in succession:

   The major scale
   The major arpeggio

When the examiner requests a **minor tonal centre**, the candidate should play in succession:

   The melodic minor scale
   The harmonic minor scale
   The minor arpeggio

or ii) Orchestral extracts

See current syllabus for details

Jazz clarinet candidates to prepare *either* section i) *or* section ii) in full

either i) Scales & arpeggios (from memory) – the examiner will select from the following:

Using the tonal/modal centres E, A♭/G♯, C **and** G: Major scale followed by major 7th arpeggio Dorian scale followed by minor 7th arpeggio Mixolydian scale followed by major arpeggio with a lowered 7th (E^7, A♭^{7}, C^7 and G^7)	E & G: three octaves A♭/G♯ and C: two octaves	min. tempi: scales: ♩=132 arpeggios: ♩.=69 7ths: ♩=104	straight *or* swung (♫ = ♩♪)	tongued, slurred *or* staccato- tongued (straight scales only)
Using the tonal centre E: Jazz melodic minor scale followed by minor arpeggio with major 7th	three octaves			
Using the tonal centre A♭: Whole tone scale followed by augmented arpeggio	two octaves			
Chromatic scale starting on E Blues scale starting on G Diminished 7th arpeggio starting on E	three octaves			
Pentatonic (major) scale starting on C Pentatonic (minor) scale starting on A♭	two octaves			

f or *p*

or ii) Study

See current syllabus for details

*Mixed articulation scales and arpeggios to be prepared with the following articulation:

C major scale (two octaves)‡ – see Grade 3

C major arpeggio (two octaves) – see Grade 3

C major 7th arpeggio (two octaves)* – see Grade 4

C harmonic minor scale (two octaves) – see Grade 5

C melodic minor scale (two octaves) – see Grade 5

C minor arpeggio (two octaves) – see Grade 5

Dorian scale on C (two octaves)* – see Grade 4

C minor 7th arpeggio (two octaves)* – see Grade 4

Mixolydian scale on C (two octaves)* – see Grade 4

C major arpeggio with a lowered 7th (C⁷) (three octaves)

Dominant 7th arpeggio in the key of C (two octaves)* – see Grade 4

C pentatonic major scale (two octaves)‡ – see Grade 5

Diminished 7th arpeggio on C (two octaves)*

E major scale (three octaves)‡

Grade 8 continued

E major arpeggio (three octaves)

E major 7th arpeggio (three octaves)*

E harmonic minor scale (three octaves)

E melodic minor scale (three octaves)

E minor arpeggio (three octaves)

E jazz melodic minor (three octaves)*

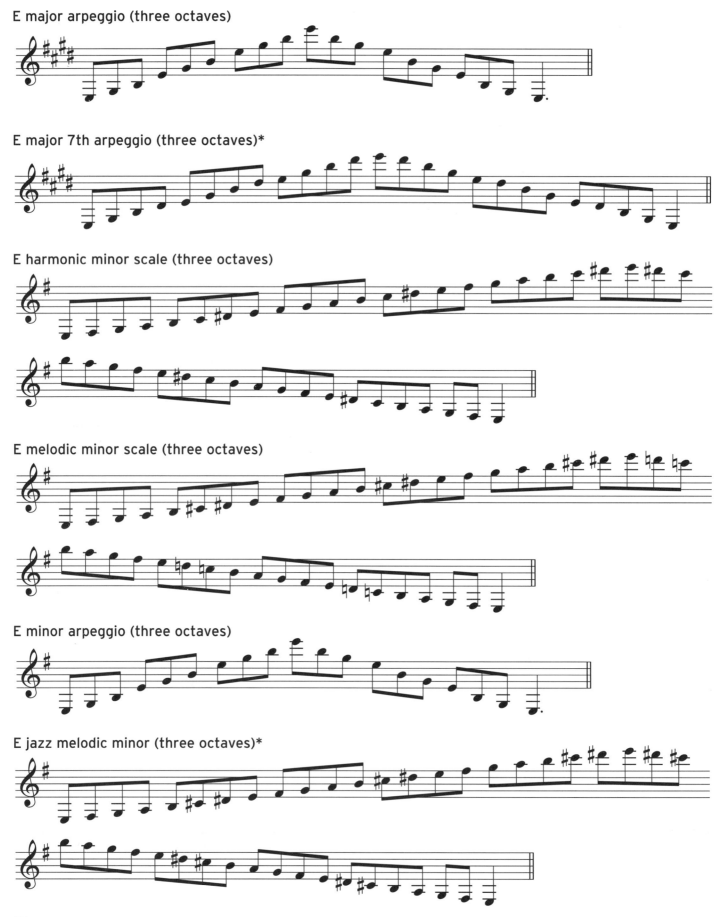

Dorian scale on E (three octaves)*

E minor 7th arpeggio (three octaves)*

Mixolydian scale on E (three octaves)*

E major arpeggio with a lowered 7th (E⁷) (three octaves)*

E minor arpeggio with a major 7th (three octaves)*

Grade 8 continued

Chromatic scale starting on E (three octaves)‡

Diminished 7th arpeggio on E (three octaves)*

G major scale (three octaves)‡

G major arpeggio (three octaves)

G major 7th arpeggio (three octaves)*

G harmonic minor scale (three octaves)

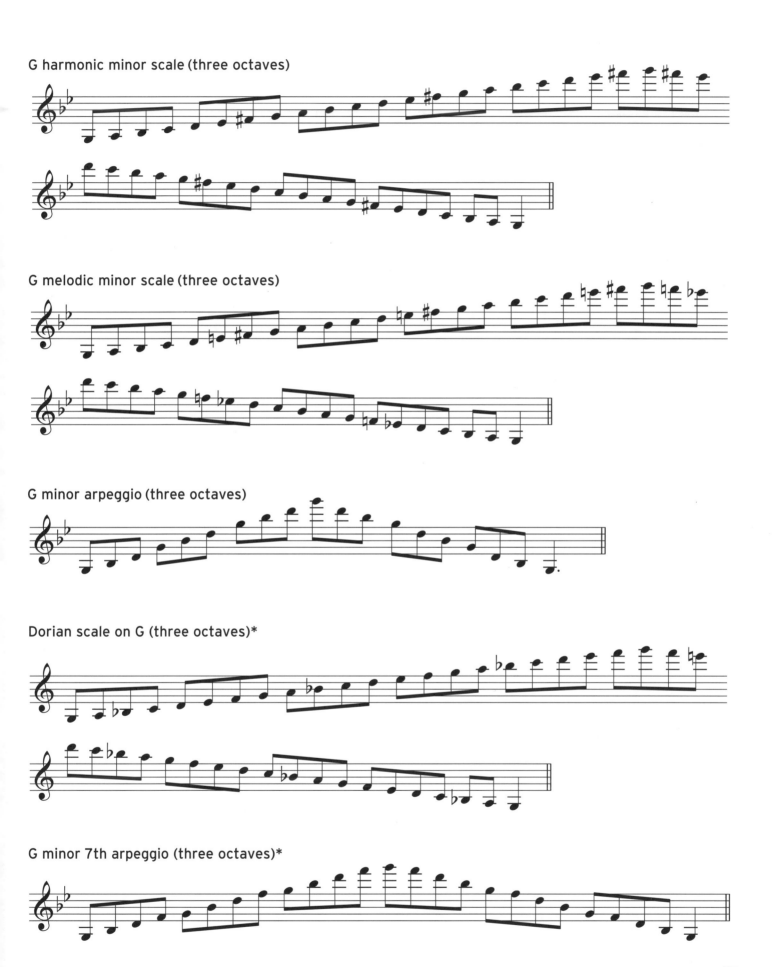

G melodic minor scale (three octaves)

G minor arpeggio (three octaves)

Dorian scale on G (three octaves)*

G minor 7th arpeggio (three octaves)*

Grade 8 continued

Mixolydian scale on G (three octaves)*

G major arpeggio with a lowered 7th (G⁷) (three octaves)*

Blues scale on G (three octaves)*

G whole-tone scale (three octaves)

A♭ major scale (two octaves)‡ – see Grade 5

A♭ major arpeggio (two octaves) – see Grade 5

A♭ major 7th arpeggio (two octaves)*

G# harmonic minor scale (two octaves)

G# melodic minor scale (two octaves)

G# minor arpeggio (two octaves)

Dorian scale on G#/A♭ (two octaves)*

G# minor 7th arpeggio (two octaves)*

Mixolydian scale on A♭/G# (two octaves)*

A♭ major arpeggio with a lowered 7th (A♭⁷) (two octaves)*

G#/A♭ pentatonic minor scale (two octaves)*

Grade 8 continued

Whole-tone scale on A♭ (two octaves)*

Augmented arpeggio on A♭ (two octaves)*

Dominant 7th arpeggio in the key of A (three octaves)

B major scale (two octaves)

B major arpeggio (two octaves)

B harmonic minor scale (two octaves) – see Grade 4

B melodic minor scale (two octaves) – see Grade 4

B minor arpeggio (two octaves) – see Grade 4

Augmented arpeggio on B (two octaves)